THE COMPLETE

BOOSEY & HAWKES

FLUTE

SCALE

Scales and Arpeggios

SCALE BOOK

BOOSEY & HAWKES

Boosey & Hawkes Music Publishers Ltd

www.boosey.com

C MAJOR

1 One Octave Scale   2 Arpeggio

3 Twelfth   4 Arpeggio

5 Two Octave Scale   6 Arpeggio

7 Three Octave Scale

8 Arpeggio

Sevenths

9 Dominant Two Octaves   10 Diminished Two Octaves

11 Diminished Three Octaves

Chromatics

12 One Octave

13 Two Octaves

14 Three Octaves

Try the scales and arpeggios in the following rhythms and articulations:

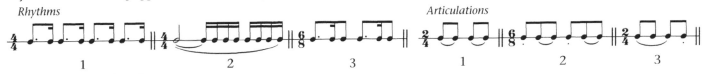

Whole Tone Scales

15 Two Octaves

16 Three Octaves

Scales in Thirds

17 One Octave

18 Two Octaves

19 Three Octaves

Broken Exercises

20 Arpeggio

21 Dominant Seventh

(or in 4's)

22 Diminished Seventh

(or in 4's)

For Further Practice

23 Interrupted Scale

etc.

24 Scale in Octaves

etc.

A MINOR

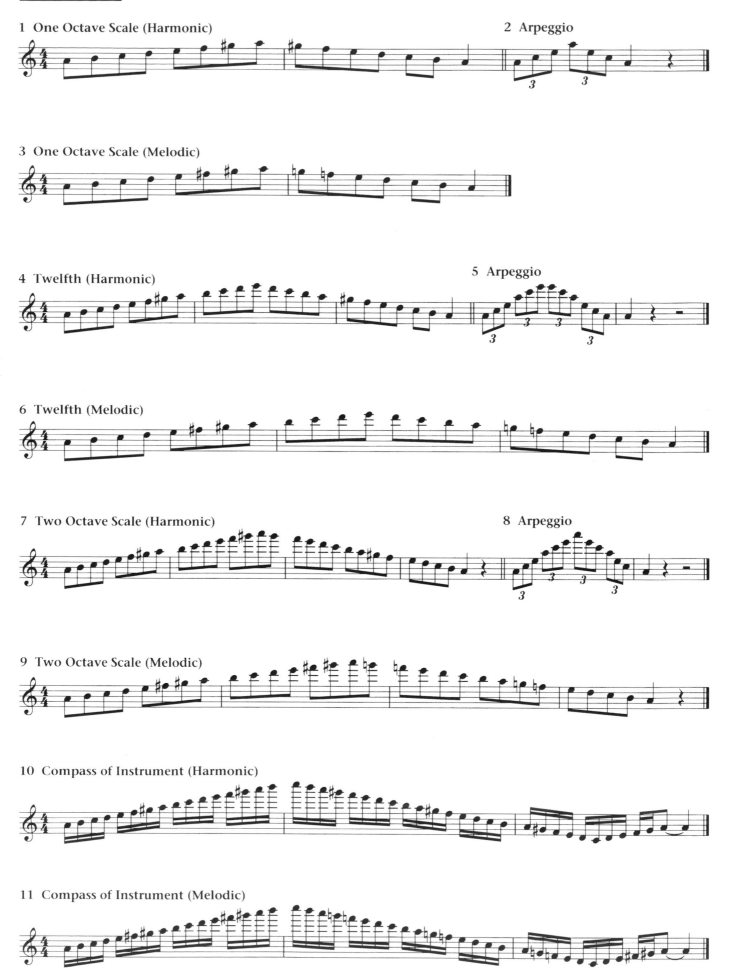

1 One Octave Scale (Harmonic)

2 Arpeggio

3 One Octave Scale (Melodic)

4 Twelfth (Harmonic)

5 Arpeggio

6 Twelfth (Melodic)

7 Two Octave Scale (Harmonic)

8 Arpeggio

9 Two Octave Scale (Melodic)

10 Compass of Instrument (Harmonic)

11 Compass of Instrument (Melodic)

Try the scales and arpeggios in the following rhythms and articulations:

Scales in Thirds (Harmonic)

12 One Octave

13 Compass of Instrument

14 Broken Arpeggio

For Further Practice

15 Interrupted Scale (Harmonic)

16 Scale in Thirds (Melodic)

17 Scale in Fourths (Melodic)

G MAJOR

1 One Octave Scale

2 Arpeggio

3 Twelfth

4 Arpeggio

5 Two Octave Scale

6 Arpeggio

7 Compass of Instrument

Sevenths

8 Dominant Two Octaves

9 Diminished Two Octaves

Chromatics

10 One Octave

11 Two Octaves

Try the scales and arpeggios in the following rhythms and articulations:

Rhythms

1   2   3

Articulations

1   2   3

Whole Tone Scales

12 Two Octaves

13 Compass of Instrument

Scales in Thirds

14 One Octave

15 Compass of Instrument

Broken Exercises

16 Arpeggio (or in 4's)

17 Dominant Seventh (or in 4's)

18 Diminished Seventh (or in 4's)

For Further Practice

19 Interrupted Scale

20 Scale in Sixths

E MINOR

1 One Octave Scale (Harmonic)

2 Arpeggio

3 One Octave Scale (Melodic)

4 Twelfth (Harmonic)

5 Arpeggio

6 Twelfth (Melodic)

7 Two Octave Scale (Harmonic)

8 Arpeggio

9 Two Octave Scale (Melodic)

10 Compass of Instrument (Harmonic)

11 Compass of Instrument (Melodic)

Try the scales and arpeggios in the following rhythms and articulations:

Scales in Thirds (Harmonic)

12 One Octave

13 Compass of Instrument

14 Broken Arpeggio

For Further Practice

15 Interrupted Scale (Harmonic)

16 Scale in Sixths (Melodic)

17 Scale in Thirds (Melodic)

etc.

18 Scale in Octaves (Melodic)

etc.

D MAJOR

1 One Octave Scale

2 Arpeggio

3 Twelfth

4 Arpeggio

5 Two Octave Scale

6 Arpeggio

7 Compass of Instrument

Sevenths

8 Dominant Two Octaves

9 Diminished Two Octaves

Chromatics

10 One Octave

11 Two Octaves

Try the scales and arpeggios in the following rhythms and articulations:

Whole Tone Scales

12 Two Octaves

13 Compass of Instrument

10

Scales in Thirds

14 One Octave

15 Compass of Instrument

Broken Exercises

16 Arpeggio

(or in 4's)

17 Dominant Seventh

(or in 4's)

18 Diminished Seventh

(or in 4's)

For Further Practice

19 Interrupted Scale

20 Scale in Fourths

B MINOR

1 One Octave Scale (Harmonic)　　　　　　　　　　　　　　　　2 Arpeggio

3 One Octave Scale (Melodic)

4 Twelfth (Harmonic)　　　　　　　　　　　　　　　　5 Arpeggio

6 Twelfth (Melodic)

7 Two Octave Scale (Harmonic)　　　　　　　　　　　　8 Arpeggio

9 Two Octave Scale (Melodic)

10 Compass of Instrument (Harmonic)

11 Compass of Instrument (Melodic)

Try the scales and arpeggios in the following rhythms and articulations:

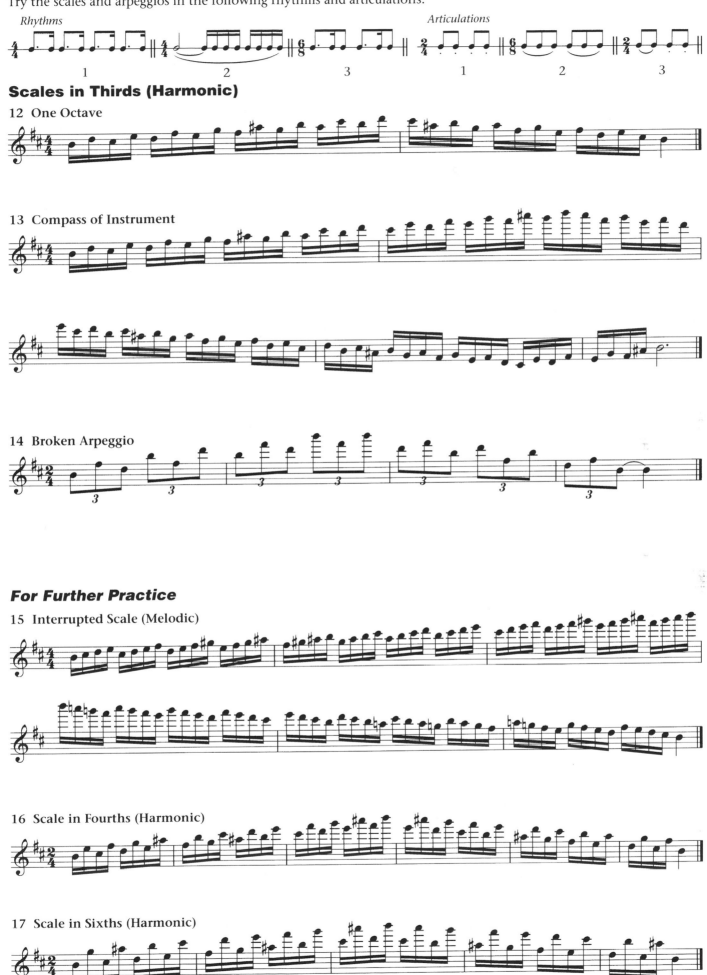

Scales in Thirds (Harmonic)

12 One Octave

13 Compass of Instrument

14 Broken Arpeggio

For Further Practice

15 Interrupted Scale (Melodic)

16 Scale in Fourths (Harmonic)

17 Scale in Sixths (Harmonic)

A MAJOR

1 One Octave Scale

2 Arpeggio

3 Twelfth

4 Arpeggio

5 Two Octave Scale

6 Arpeggio

7 Compass of Instrument

Sevenths

8 Dominant Two Octaves

9 Diminished Two Octaves

Chromatics

10 One Octave

11 Two Octaves

Try the scales and arpeggios in the following rhythms and articulations:

Rhythms   *Articulations*

1   2   3   1   2   3

Whole Tone Scales

12 Two Octaves

13 Compass of Instrument

14

Scales in Thirds

14 One Octave

15 Compass of Instrument

Broken Exercises

16 Arpeggio (or in 4's)

17 Dominant Seventh (or in 4's)

18 Diminished Seventh (or in 4's)

For Further Practice

19 Interrupted Scale

20 Blues Scale

F♯ MINOR

1 One Octave Scale (Harmonic)

2 Arpeggio

3 One Octave Scale (Melodic)

4 Twelfth (Harmonic)

5 Arpeggio

6 Twelfth (Melodic)

7 Two Octave Scale (Harmonic)

8 Arpeggio

9 Two Octave Scale (Melodic)

10 Compass of Instrument (Harmonic)

11 Compass of Instrument (Melodic)

Try the scales and arpeggios in the following rhythms and articulations:

Scales in Thirds (Harmonic)

12 One Octave

13 Compass of Instrument

14 Broken Arpeggio

For Further Practice

15 Interrupted Scale (Harmonic)

16 Scale in Thirds (Melodic)

17 Scale in Fourths (Melodic)

E MAJOR

1 One Octave Scale

2 Arpeggio

3 Twelfth

4 Arpeggio

5 Two Octave Scale

6 Arpeggio

7 Compass of Instrument

Sevenths

8 Dominant Two Octaves

9 Diminished Two Octaves

Chromatics

10 One Octave

11 Two Octaves

Try the scales and arpeggios in the following rhythms and articulations:

Whole Tone Scales

12 Two Octaves

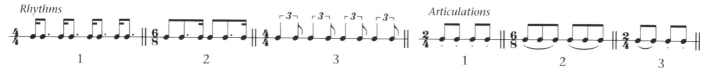

13 Compass of Instrument

18

Scales in Thirds

14 One Octave

15 Compass of Instrument

Broken Exercises

16 Arpeggio

(or in 4's)

17 Dominant Seventh

(or in 4's)

18 Diminished Seventh

(or in 4's)

For Further Practice

19 Interrupted Scale

20 Scale in Sixths

C# MINOR

1 One Octave Scale (Harmonic)　　　　　　　　　　　　　　　　　2 Arpeggio

3 One Octave Scale (Melodic)

4 Twelfth (Harmonic)　　　　　　　　　　　　　　　　　　　5 Arpeggio

6 Twelfth (Melodic)

7 Two Octave Scale (Harmonic)　　　　　　　　　　　　　　　8 Arpeggio

9 Two Octave Scale (Melodic)

10 Compass of Instrument (Harmonic)

11 Compass of Instrument (Melodic)

Try the scales and arpeggios in the following rhythms and articulations:

Scales in Thirds (Harmonic)

12 One Octave

13 Compass of Instrument

14 Broken Arpeggio

For Further Practice

15 Interrupted Scale (Harmonic)

16 Scale in Sixths (Melodic)

17 Scale in Thirds (Melodic)

etc.

18 Scale in Octaves (Melodic)

etc.

B MAJOR

1 One Octave Scale

2 Arpeggio

3 Twelfth

4 Arpeggio

5 Two Octave Scale

6 Arpeggio

7 Compass of Instrument

Sevenths

8 Dominant Two Octaves

9 Diminished Two Octaves

Chromatics

10 One Octave

11 Two Octaves

Try the scales and arpeggios in the following rhythms and articulations:

Rhythms

Articulations

1   2   3   1   2   3

Whole Tone Scales

12 Two Octaves

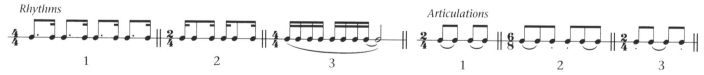

13 Compass of Instrument

Scales in Thirds

14 One Octave

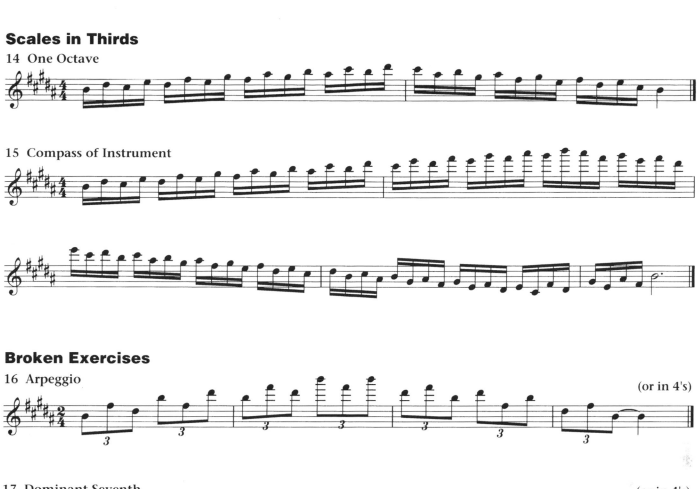

15 Compass of Instrument

Broken Exercises

16 Arpeggio (or in 4's)

17 Dominant Seventh (or in 4's)

18 Diminished Seventh (or in 4's)

For Further Practice

19 Interrupted Scale

20 Scale in Fourths

G♯ MINOR

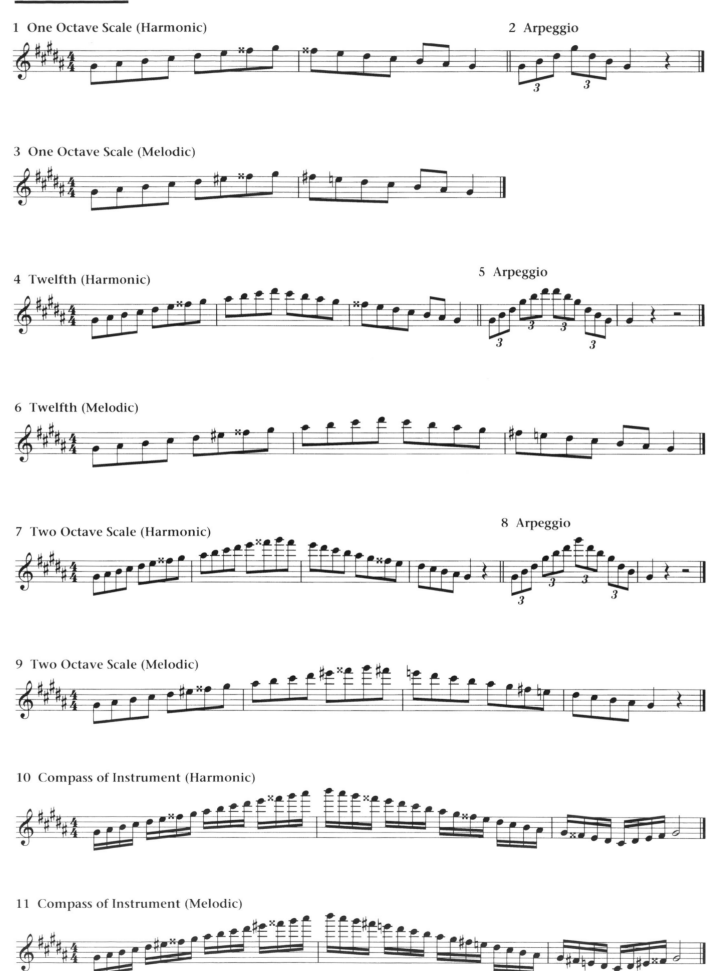

1 One Octave Scale (Harmonic) 2 Arpeggio

3 One Octave Scale (Melodic)

4 Twelfth (Harmonic) 5 Arpeggio

6 Twelfth (Melodic)

7 Two Octave Scale (Harmonic) 8 Arpeggio

9 Two Octave Scale (Melodic)

10 Compass of Instrument (Harmonic)

11 Compass of Instrument (Melodic)

Try the scales and arpeggios in the following rhythms and articulations:

Scales in Thirds (Harmonic)

12 One Octave

13 Compass of Instrument

14 Broken Arpeggio

For Further Practice

15 Interrupted Scale (Melodic)

16 Scale in Fourths (Harmonic)

17 Scale in Sixths (Harmonic)

F♯ MAJOR

1 One Octave Scale　　　　　　　　　　　　　　　　　　　　　　**2 Arpeggio**

3 Twelfth　　　　　　　　　　　　　　　　　　　　　　　　　　**4 Arpeggio**

5 Two Octave Scale　　　　　　　　　　　　　　　　　　　　　　**6 Arpeggio**

7 Compass of Instrument

Sevenths

8 Dominant Two Octaves　　　　　　　　　**9 Diminished Two Octaves**

Chromatics

10 One Octave

11 Two Octaves

Try the scales and arpeggios in the following rhythms and articulations:

Whole Tone Scales

12 Two Octaves

13 Compass of Instrument

26

Scales in Thirds

14 One Octave

15 Compass of Instrument

Broken Exercises

16 Arpeggio

(or in 4's)

17 Dominant Seventh

(or in 4's)

18 Diminished Seventh

(or in 4's)

For Further Practice

19 Interrupted Scale

20 Blues Scale

E♭ MINOR

1 One Octave Scale (Harmonic) **2 Arpeggio**

3 One Octave Scale (Melodic)

4 Twelfth (Harmonic) **5 Arpeggio**

6 Twelfth (Melodic)

7 Two Octave Scale (Harmonic) **8 Arpeggio**

9 Two Octave Scale (Melodic)

10 Compass of Instrument (Harmonic)

11 Compass of Instrument (Melodic)

Try the scales and arpeggios in the following rhythms and articulations:

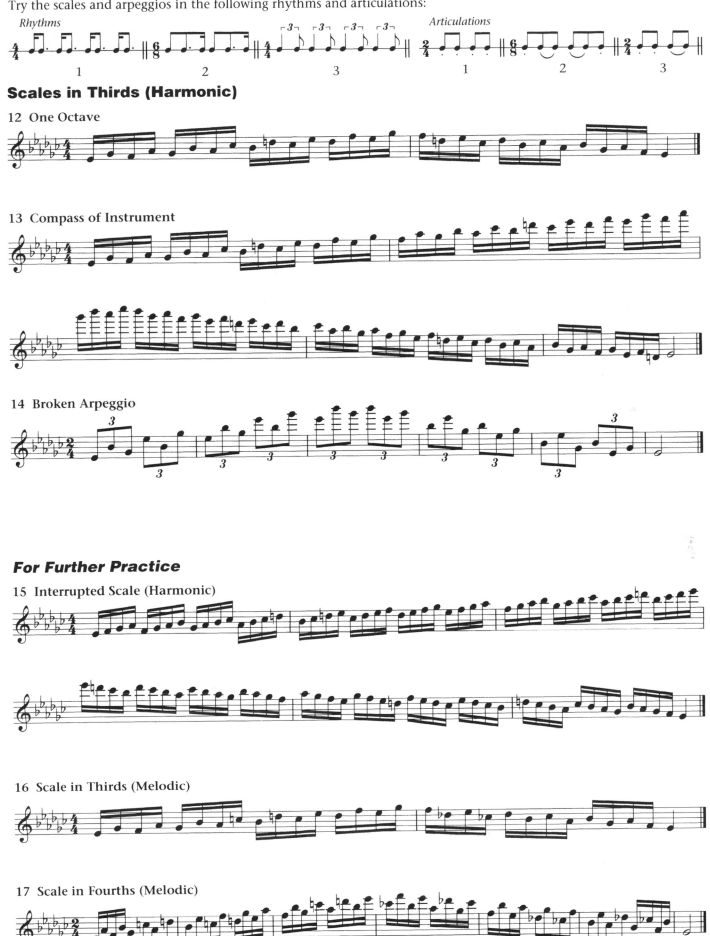

Scales in Thirds (Harmonic)

12 One Octave

13 Compass of Instrument

14 Broken Arpeggio

For Further Practice

15 Interrupted Scale (Harmonic)

16 Scale in Thirds (Melodic)

17 Scale in Fourths (Melodic)

D♭ MAJOR

1 One Octave Scale
2 Arpeggio

3 Twelfth
4 Arpeggio

5 Two Octave Scale
6 Arpeggio

7 Compass of Instrument

Sevenths

8 Dominant Two Octaves
9 Diminished Two Octaves

Chromatics

10 One Octave

11 Two Octaves

Try the scales and arpeggios in the following rhythms and articulations:

Whole Tone Scales

12 Two Octaves

13 Compass of Instrument

Scales in Thirds

14 One Octave

15 Compass of Instrument

Broken Exercises

16 Arpeggio

(or in 4's)

17 Dominant Seventh

(or in 4's)

18 Diminished Seventh

(or in 4's)

For Further Practice

19 Interrupted Scale

20 Scale in Sixths

B♭ MINOR

1 One Octave Scale (Harmonic)   **2 Arpeggio**

3 One Octave Scale (Melodic)

4 Twelfth (Harmonic)   **5 Arpeggio**

6 Twelfth (Melodic)

7 Two Octave Scale (Harmonic)   **8 Arpeggio**

9 Two Octave Scale (Melodic)

10 Compass of Instrument (Harmonic)

11 Compass of Instrument (Melodic)

Try the scales and arpeggios in the following rhythms and articulations:

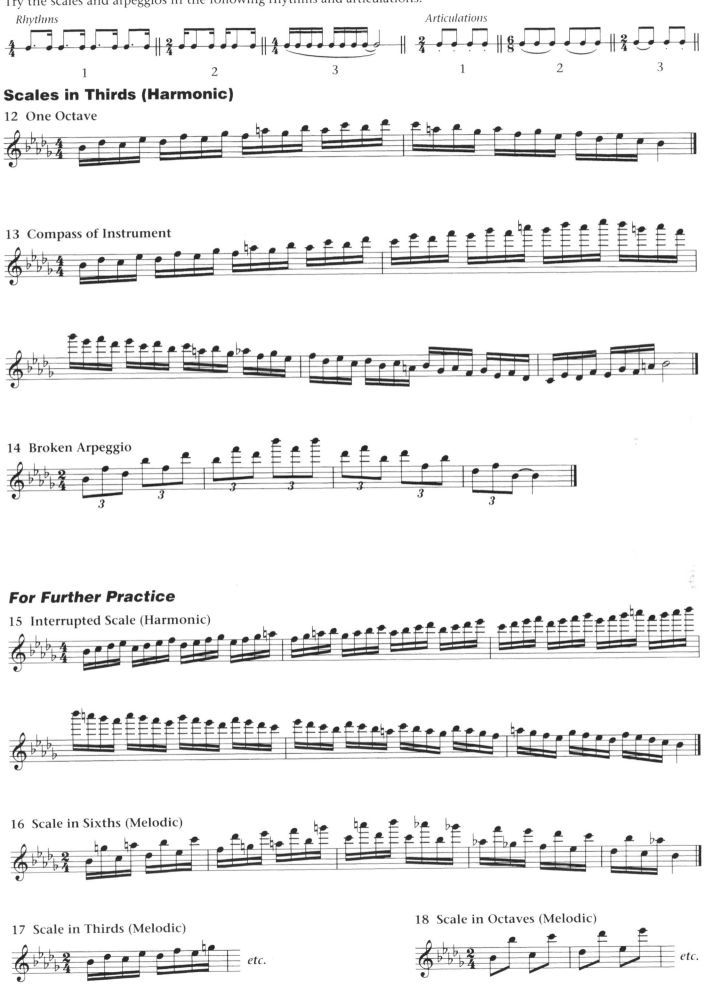

Scales in Thirds (Harmonic)

12 One Octave

13 Compass of Instrument

14 Broken Arpeggio

For Further Practice

15 Interrupted Scale (Harmonic)

16 Scale in Sixths (Melodic)

17 Scale in Thirds (Melodic)

etc.

18 Scale in Octaves (Melodic)

etc.

A♭ MAJOR

1 One Octave Scale

2 Arpeggio

3 Twelfth

4 Arpeggio

5 Two Octave Scale

6 Arpeggio

7 Compass of Instrument

Sevenths

8 Dominant Two Octaves

9 Diminished Two Octaves

Chromatics

10 One Octave

11 Two Octaves

Try the scales and arpeggios in the following rhythms and articulations:

Rhythms

1

2

3

Articulations

1

2

3

Whole Tone Scales

12 Two Octaves

13 Compass of Instrument

34

Scales in Thirds

14 One Octave

15 Compass of Instrument

Broken Exercises

16 Arpeggio

(or in 4's)

17 Dominant Seventh

(or in 4's)

18 Diminished Seventh

(or in 4's)

For Further Practice

19 Interrupted Scale

20 Scale in Fourths

F MINOR

1 One Octave Scale (Harmonic)   2 Arpeggio

3 One Octave Scale (Melodic)

4 Twelfth (Harmonic)   5 Arpeggio

6 Twelfth (Melodic)

7 Two Octave Scale (Harmonic)   8 Arpeggio

9 Two Octave Scale (Melodic)

10 Compass of Instrument (Harmonic)

11 Compass of Instrument (Melodic)

Try the scales and arpeggios in the following rhythms and articulations:

Scales in Thirds (Harmonic)

12 One Octave

13 Compass of Instrument

14 Broken Arpeggio

For Further Practice

15 Interrupted Scale (Melodic)

16 Scale in Fourths (Harmonic)

17 Scale in Sixths (Harmonic)

E♭ MAJOR

1 One Octave Scale   **2 Arpeggio**

3 Twelfth   **4 Arpeggio**

5 Two Octave Scale   **6 Arpeggio**

7 Compass of Instrument

Sevenths

8 Dominant Two Octaves   **9 Diminished Two Octaves**

Chromatics

10 One Octave

11 Two Octaves

Try the scales and arpeggios in the following rhythms and articulations:

Rhythms   *Articulations*

1   2   3   1   2   3

Whole Tone Scales

12 Two Octaves

13 Compass of Instrument

Scales in Thirds

14 One Octave

15 Compass of Instrument

Broken Exercises

16 Arpeggio

(or in 4's)

17 Dominant Seventh

(or in 4's)

18 Diminished Seventh

(or in 4's)

For Further Practice

19 Interrupted Scale

20 Blues Scale

C MINOR

1 One Octave Scale (Harmonic)   **2 Arpeggio**

3 One Octave Scale (Melodic)

4 Twelfth (Harmonic)   **5 Arpeggio**

6 Twelfth (Melodic)

7 Two Octave Scale (Harmonic)   **8 Arpeggio**

9 Two Octave Scale (Melodic)

10 Three Octave Scale (Harmonic)

11 Three Octave Scale (Melodic)

12 Three Octave Arpeggio

Try the scales and arpeggios in the following rhythms and articulations:

Scales in Thirds (Harmonic)

13 One Octave

14 Two Octaves

15 Three Octaves

16 Broken Arpeggio

For Further Practice

17 Chromatic in Thirds

B♭ MAJOR

1 One Octave Scale

2 Arpeggio

3 Twelfth

4 Arpeggio

5 Two Octave Scale

6 Arpeggio

7 Compass of Instrument

Sevenths

8 Dominant Two Octaves

9 Diminished Two Octaves

Chromatics

10 One Octave

11 Two Octaves

Try the scales and arpeggios in the following rhythms and articulations:

Rhythms   *Articulations*

1   2   3   1   2   3

Whole Tone Scales

12 Two Octaves

13 Compass of Instrument

Scales in Thirds

14 One Octave

15 Compass of Instrument

Broken Exercises

16 Arpeggio

(or in 4's)

17 Dominant Seventh

(or in 4's)

18 Diminished Seventh

(or in 4's)

For Further Practice

19 Interrupted Scale

20 Scale in Sixths

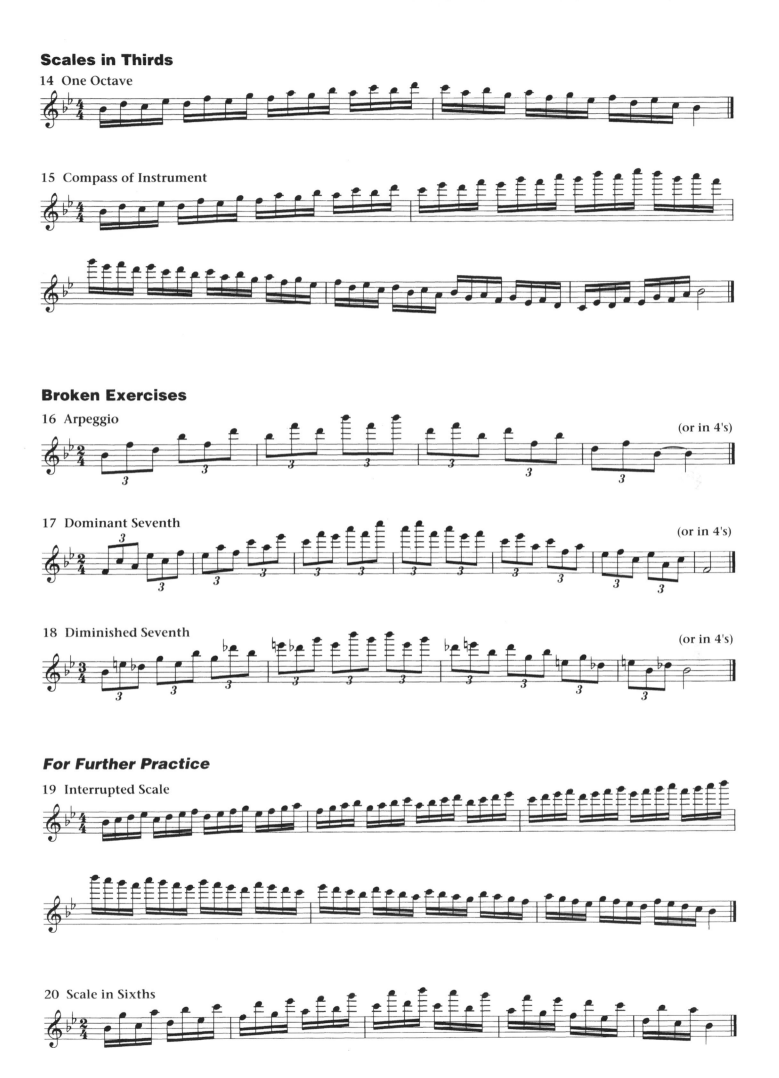

G MINOR

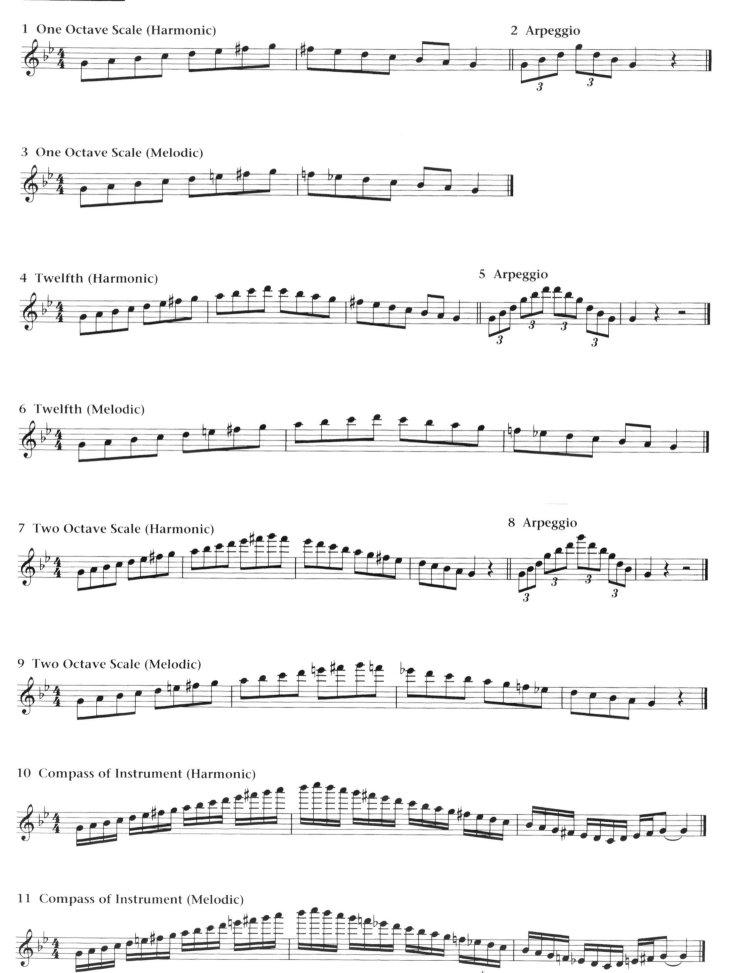

1 One Octave Scale (Harmonic) 2 Arpeggio

3 One Octave Scale (Melodic)

4 Twelfth (Harmonic) 5 Arpeggio

6 Twelfth (Melodic)

7 Two Octave Scale (Harmonic) 8 Arpeggio

9 Two Octave Scale (Melodic)

10 Compass of Instrument (Harmonic)

11 Compass of Instrument (Melodic)

Try the scales and arpeggios in the following rhythms and articulations:

Scales in Thirds (Harmonic)

12 One Octave

13 Compass of Instrument

14 Broken Arpeggio

For Further Practice

15 Interrupted Scale (Harmonic)

16 Scale in Sixths (Melodic)

17 Scale in Thirds (Melodic)

etc.

18 Scale in Octaves (Melodic)

etc.

F MAJOR

1 One Octave Scale

2 Arpeggio

3 Twelfth

4 Arpeggio

5 Two Octave Scale

6 Arpeggio

7 Compass of Instrument

Sevenths

8 Dominant Two Octaves

9 Diminished Two Octaves

Chromatics

10 One Octave

11 Two Octaves

Try the scales and arpeggios in the following rhythms and articulations:

Whole Tone Scales

12 Two Octaves

13 Compass of Instrument

Scales in Thirds

14 One Octave

15 Compass of Instrument

Broken Exercises

16 Arpeggio

(or in 4's)

17 Dominant Seventh

(or in 4's)

18 Diminished Seventh

(or in 4's)

For Further Practice

19 Interrupted Scale

20 Scale in Fourths

D MINOR

1 One Octave Scale (Harmonic)   2 Arpeggio

3 One Octave Scale (Melodic)

4 Twelfth (Harmonic)   5 Arpeggio

6 Twelfth (Melodic)

7 Two Octave Scale (Harmonic)   8 Arpeggio

9 Two Octave Scale (Melodic)

10 Compass of Instrument (Harmonic)

11 Compass of Instrument (Melodic)

Try the scales and arpeggios in the following rhythms and articulations:

Scales in Thirds (Harmonic)

12 One Octave

13 Compass of Instrument

14 Broken Arpeggio

For Further Practice

15 Interrupted Scale (Melodic)

16 Scale in Fourths (Harmonic)

17 Scale in Sixths (Harmonic)

Printed by Halstan:
Halstan UK, 2–10 Plantation Road, Amersham, Bucks, HP6 6HJ. United Kingdom
Halstan DE, Weißliliengasse 4, 55116 Mainz. Germany

PRACTICE PLANNER

Key	Nos.	Week											
		1	2	3	4	5	6	7	8	9	10	11	12
C major													
A minor													
G major													
E minor													
D major													
B minor													
A major													
F♯ minor													
E major													
C♯ minor													
B major													
G♯ minor													
F♯ major													
E♭ minor													
D♭ major													
B♭ minor													
A♭ major													
F minor													
E♭ major													
C minor													
B♭ major													
G minor													
F major													
D minor													
		1	2	3	4	5	6	7	8	9	10	11	12

Comments:

Music set by Stave Origination
Cover by Russell Stretten Design